For Childhood Friends Everywhere

Paper Republic LLC
7548 Ravenna Ave NE, Seattle, Washington 98115
Text and illustration copyright © 2014 by Wenzheng Fu
English translation copyright © 2016 by China Educational Publications Import & Export Corporation Ltd.
Simplified Chinese-English edition copyright © 2016 by China Educational Publications Import & Export Corporation Ltd.
Publication Consultant: Roxanne Hsu Feldman
Published by Paper Republic LLC, by arrangement with Zhejiang Juvenile and Children's Publishing House Co., Ltd.
All rights reserved, including the right of reproduction in whole or in part in any form.
Printed and bound in China.
ISBN 978-1-945-29501-0

The illustrations in this book were rendered in gouache.
For more titles from Candied Plums and additional features, please visit www.candiedplums.com.

我 讨 厌 宝 弟
Buddy Is So Annoying

by Wenzheng Fu   translated by Adam Lanphier

Candied Plums

上幼儿园的第一天，我就认识了宝弟。

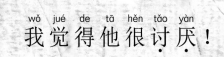

wǒ jué de tā hěn tǎo yàn
我觉得他很讨厌！

他慢吞吞的时候很讨厌。

tā dòng zuò kuài de shí hou yě hěn tǎo yàn
他动作快的时候也很讨厌。

他说话的时候很讨厌。

他不说话的时候更讨厌。

bú guò ǒu ěr wǒ huì wàng le tǎo yàn bǎo dì
不过偶尔，我会忘了讨厌宝弟。

dàn jī běn shang wǒ hái shi hěn tǎo yàn bǎo dì
但基本上，我还是很讨厌宝弟！

tā zhēn de hěn fán rén

他真的很烦人！

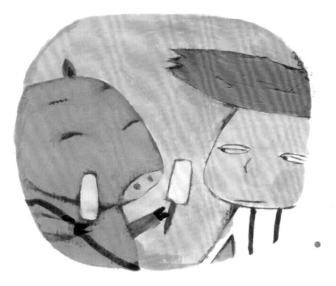

不过偶尔……被他烦一下也不错。

你知道有时候吧，得有人陪着你。

不许欺负他！

wǒ shì bù dé yǐ cái ràng tā péi zhe de
我是不得已才让他陪着的。

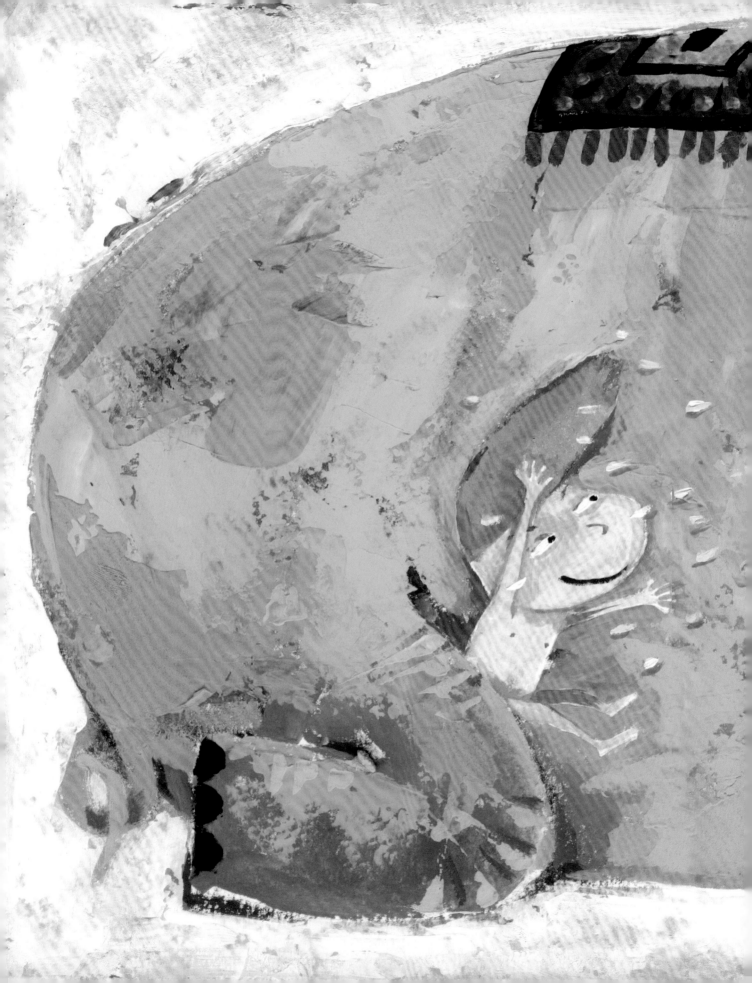

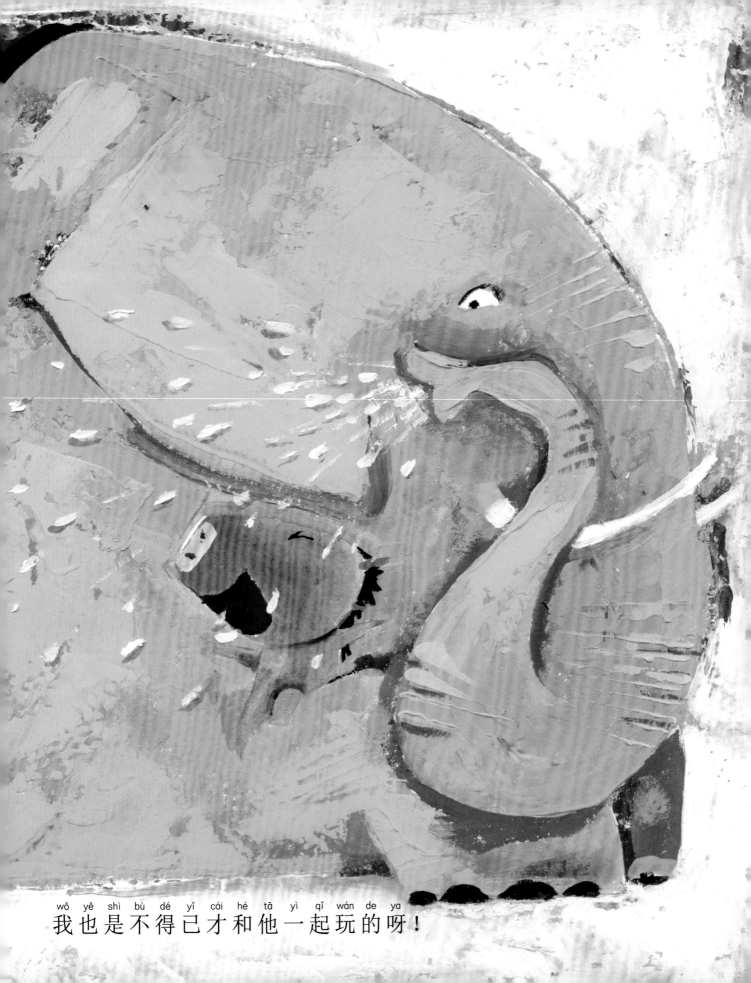

wǒ yě shì bù dé yǐ cái hé tā yì qǐ wán de ya
我也是不得已才和他一起玩的呀！

没想到，一玩就玩了很久。

但这还是不能改变我讨厌宝弟这个事实。

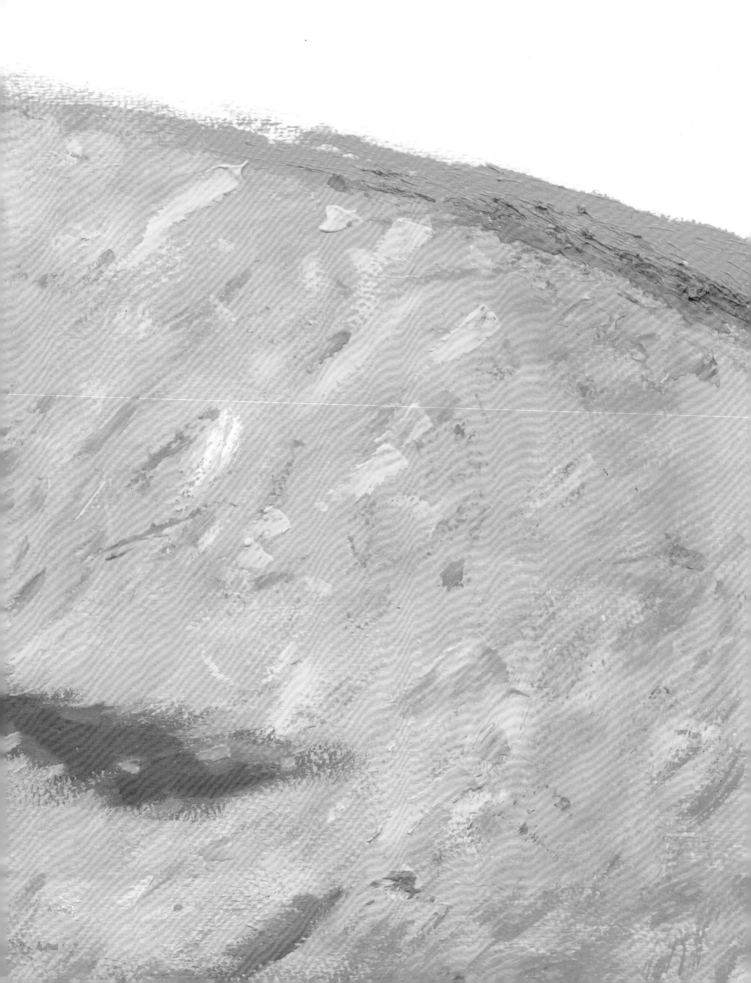

tā bù shuō huà de yàng zi hái shi tǐng tǎo yàn de
他不说话的样子还是挺讨厌的……

他说话的时候也还是那么让人讨厌。

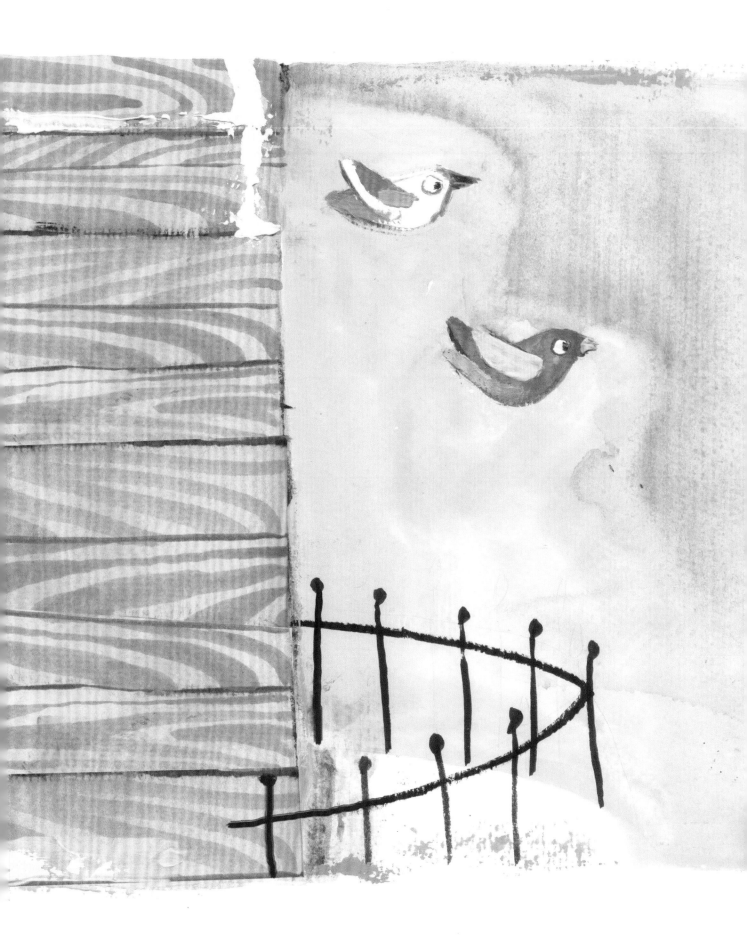

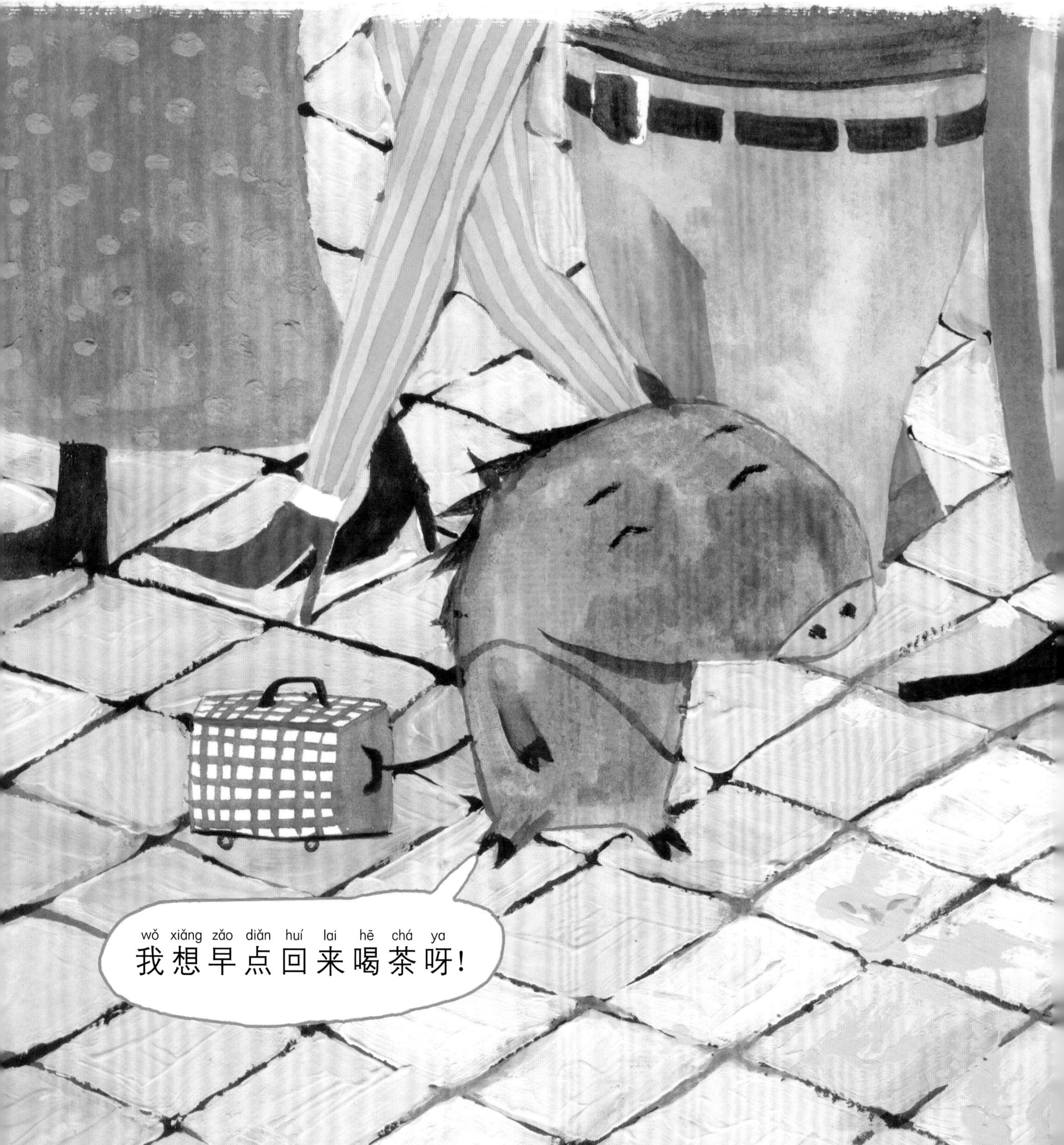
wǒ xiǎng zǎo diǎn huí lai hē chá ya
我想早点回来喝茶呀!

wǒ zhǐ shì ǒu ěr wàng le tǎo yàn bǎo dì o
我只是偶尔忘了讨厌宝弟哦！

后来，在很长的一段时间里，我都不得不让宝弟陪着我。你问我还讨厌他吗？

tǎo yàn a　　dàn shì nǐ zhī dào　　yǒu rén yuàn yì zhè yàng cháng jiǔ
讨厌啊！但是你知道，有人愿意这样长久
de péi zhe nǐ　　ràng nǐ tǎo yàn　　shì yí jiàn duō me xìng yùn de shì
地陪着你，让你讨厌，是一件多么幸运的事！

Words and Expressions

幼儿园	yòu ér yuán	kindergarten
讨厌	tǎo yàn	*adj.* annoying
		v. to feel annoyed
等等我	děng děng wǒ	Wait for me!
过线	guò xiàn	to cross the line
你赔！	nǐ péi	You're replacing this!
偶尔	ǒu ěr	once in a while
基本上	jī běn shang	on the whole
也不错	yě bú cuò	not bad
陪着	péi zhe	to keep (someone) company
欺负	qī fu	to pick on (someone)
不得已	bù dé yǐ	have to
没想到	méi xiǎng dào	to one's surprise
改变	gǎi biàn	to change
事实	shì shí	fact
海浪	hǎi làng	sea wave
有什么了不起	yǒu shén me liǎo bu qǐ	That's nothing.
幸运	xìng yùn	lucky and wonderful
石头，剪刀，布！	shí tou jiǎn dāo bù	Rock, paper, scissors!

For more language learning resources, please visit our website at www.candiedplums.com.

Buddy Is So Annoying

"Hey! I'm Buddy."
I've known Buddy since the first day of kindergarten.

I think he's so annoying.

"Wait for me! Wait for me!"
He's annoying when he can't keep up.

He's also annoying when he's faster than me.

"You can't cross this line!"
He's annoying when he talks.

"You're replacing this!" "Humph!"
And more annoying when he doesn't talk.

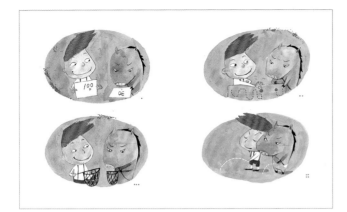

Once in a while, I forget how annoying he is.

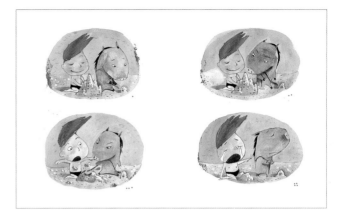

But on the whole, he's definitely annoying.

He really bugs me.

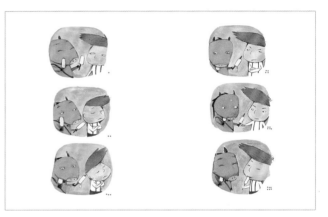

But once in a while, being bugged isn't so bad.

You know how it is. Sometimes you need someone by your side.

"Stop picking on him!"

I only let him hang around when I have to.

And I only play with him when I have to.

But then, before I know it, we'll have been playing for a long time.

But this doesn't change the fact that Buddy is annoying.

"I'll be back really soon!"

The way he looks when he's not talking is still so annoying…

And when he talks, it's as annoying as ever.

"The waves here are three stories tall!"

"That's nothing. I've seen waves that are ten stories tall!"

"How come he's still not back…"

"Buddy! Didn't you say you wouldn't be back until next week?"

"I thought I'd come back early for a cup of tea!"

Man, he is so annoying when he's early! Haha!

It's just that I sometimes forget to be annoyed.

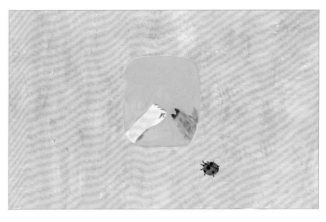

For a long time after that, I let Buddy hang around. Does that mean he doesn't annoy me?

Nope! He still annoys me. But do you know what? Having someone around to keep you company and annoy you is a wonderful thing.

"Rock, paper, scissors!"
"Paper!"